Something deadly is roaming the mining tunnels of Janus VI, damaging equipment and killing men.

The Starship *Enterprise* responds to a distress signal from the mining colony and Kirk, Spock and McCoy are plunged into one of their more bizarre adventures as they race against time to save human lives, the colony...and something they did not expect to find. Aware of his peril, Spock moves alone through uncharted regions of the soul, in order to discover the astonishing truth about...

**THE DEVIL IN THE DARK**

D1598375

OTHER **STAR TREK FOTONOVELS**™
YOU WILL ENJOY:

*CITY ON THE
EDGE OF FOREVER*

*WHERE NO MAN
HAS GONE BEFORE*

*THE TROUBLE
WITH TRIBBLES*

*A TASTE
OF ARMAGEDDON*

*METAMORPHOSIS*

*ALL OUR YESTERDAYS*

*GALILEO SEVEN*

*A PIECE OF THE ACTION*

# STAR TREK ™*

# DEVIL IN THE DARK

written by **GENE L. COON**

adapted from the television series
created by **GENE RODDENBERRY**

$$\text{RLI:} \quad \frac{\text{VLM 6 (VLR 5–7)}}{\text{IL 5+}}$$

DEVIL IN THE DARK
*A Bantam Book / July 1978*

*Designed and produced by*
*Michael Parrish, Los Angeles*

*Star Trek™ designates a trademark of*
*Paramount Pictures Corporation.*

*Fotonovel™ designates a trademark of*
*Mandala Productions.*

ISBN 0-553-12021-2

*Published simultaneously in the United States and Canada*

PRINTED IN THE UNITED STATES OF AMERICA

0 9 8 7 6 5 4 3 2 1

Dear Readers,

As ever we are pleased and eager to hear from you in the form of letters and correspondence regarding our Star Trek Fotonovels. On the next few pages you will find some representative letters.

Your comments, suggestions and questions are more than welcome. Our new address is:

Mandala Productions
8831 Sunset Blvd., Penthouse West
Los Angeles, Ca. 90069

If you would like us to consider printing your letter in one of our future books, please include permission in writing.

Best regards,

Mandala Productions

---

Dear Mandala Productions,

Star Trek fans have been teased by rumors of a new series or a movie, but here at last is a revival in a splendid new format. I refer, of course, to your Fotonovels. You have given us the same great stories and characters we have grown to love so well, but we can now hold them in our hands and linger over our favorite scenes. Those delightful expressions and scenery no longer flash by our straining eyes and are gone, but are there preserved for us to peek at whenever the mood is upon us.

The transition from screen to page has been thoughtfully and tastefully handled, and the difficult task of maintaining continuity has been very successfully accomplished by the insertion of descriptive passages and "thought balloons." Very well done, Mandala.

Congratulations and please keep it up.

Rosemary Rawlinson
Oxford, England

Dear Mandala Productions,

I have just purchased my 4th Star Trek FOTONOVEL "A TASTE OF ARMAGEDDON." I am pleased, as I am sure many other fellow "Trekkies" are in seeing that these wonderfully entertaining books are continuing to be published.

However, I wish that you would publish more stories featuring Mr. Spock. It always made me mad that Captain Kirk has always been in the limelight and Mr. Spock has always had to take the back seat, especially with the woman characters. Without Mr. Spock's special abilities, Captain Kirk would have to deal with many more complications and disasters aboard the Enterprise. Please include more Fotonovels that focus on Mr. Spock.

Keep up the Good Work,
Wayne Howard
Omaha, Nebraska


Dear Sirs,

I would just like to express my family's pleasure in your FOTONOVEL series. Recently I found a Star Trek Novel in my son's room and began leafing through it. Though I rarely watch Star Trek, I found the story and color pictures quite enjoyable.

Since then both my husband and 15-year-old daughter have begun to enjoy the Fotonovels as well.

Sincerely,
Paulette Rivers
Dallas, Texas


Dear Mandala Productions,

Thanks for the Star Trek Fotonovels. You've captured the essence of the amazing show that was somehow greater than the sum of its parts. It's a treat to be able to pause over settings, costumes and nuances of expression. Your treatment is tasteful, reflecting care and a respect for the original that gladdens the heart of this fan.

Would it be possible to publish more "behind-the-scenes" interviews with people like make-up artists, costume and set designers, etc.?

Live long and prosper,
Vince Salvatorio
Newark, New Jersey

# CAST LIST

### James T. Kirk, Captain
### William Shatner

A man in his mid-30's whose strong independent nature and sympathetic soul make him a natural leader. His overriding concern is always the safety and well-being of his ship and its crew.

### Mr. Spock, First Officer
### Leonard Nimoy

Of Vulcan and Terran heritage, which accounts for his highly analytical mind and extraordinary strength. His life is ruled by reason and logic.

### Leonard McCoy, M.D.
### Lt. Commander
### DeForest Kelley

Senior Ship's Surgeon. Though surrounded by the most advanced equipment the 25th century can offer, he still practices medicine more with his heart than his mind.

### Montgomery Scott
### Lt. Commander
### James Doohan

### Chief Engineer Vanderberg
### Ken Lynch

### Lt. Commander Giotto
### Barry Russo

### Schmitter
### Biff Elliott

### Ed Appel
### Brad Weston

### Horta
### James Prohaska

# THE DEVIL
# IN THE DARK

## SPACE:

## THE FINAL FRONTIER

THESE ARE THE VOYAGES
OF THE STARSHIP
"ENTERPRISE." ITS
FIVE YEAR MISSION: TO
EXPLORE STRANGE NEW
WORLDS...TO SEEK OUT
NEW LIFE AND NEW CIVI-
LIZATIONS...TO
BOLDLY GO WHERE NO MAN
HAS GONE BEFORE.

## CAPTAIN'S LOG:

### STARDATE 3196.1

WE ARE ENROUTE TO JANUS VI IN
RESPONSE TO A DISTRESS SIGNAL
FROM THE PERGIUM PRODUCTION
STATION LOCATED BENEATH THE
SURFACE OF THE PLANET.

*Deep in the labyrinth of tunnels
extending from the pergium
processing plant, an anxious
guard is relieved of his duty.*

Left alone with his fears, Schmitter begins to see shapes in the shadows...ghastly images...swirling up through the subliminal stew of primordial nightmares.

Suddenly, one of the shadows moves away from the tunnel wall and Schmitter stands face to face with horror...

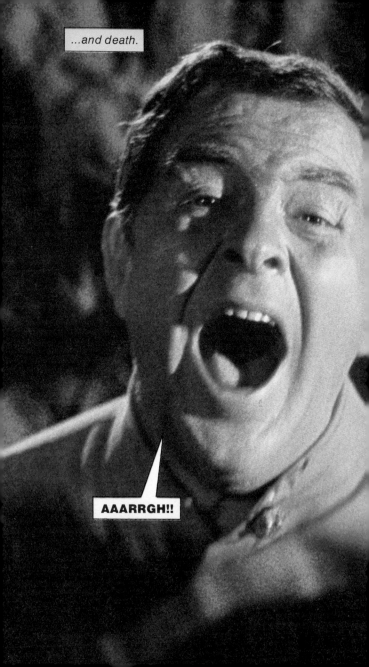

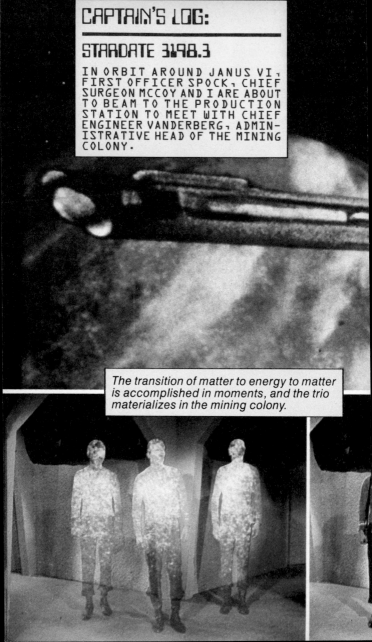

# CAPTAIN'S LOG:

## STARDATE 3198.3

IN ORBIT AROUND JANUS VI, FIRST OFFICER SPOCK, CHIEF SURGEON McCOY AND I ARE ABOUT TO BEAM TO THE PRODUCTION STATION TO MEET WITH CHIEF ENGINEER VANDERBERG, ADMIN-ISTRATIVE HEAD OF THE MINING COLONY.

*The transition of matter to energy to matter is accomplished in moments, and the trio materializes in the mining colony.*

*Once led to Chief Vanderberg's office, they are briefed on the incredible series of events that has resulted in the distress call.*

About three months ago, we opened up a new level. Sensors showed unusually high mineral levels...a real treasure house.

We are all aware that if mining conditions were not so difficult, Janus VI could supply the mineral needs of a thousand planets.

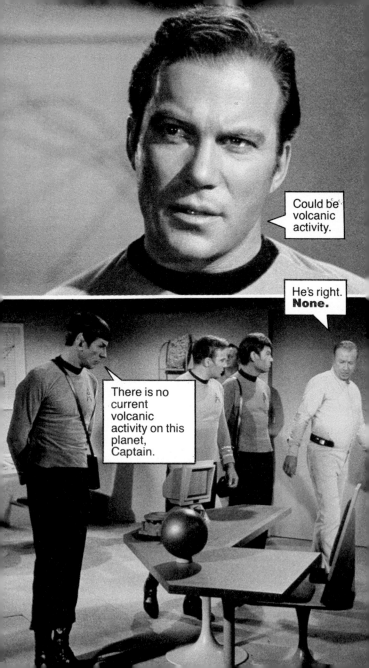

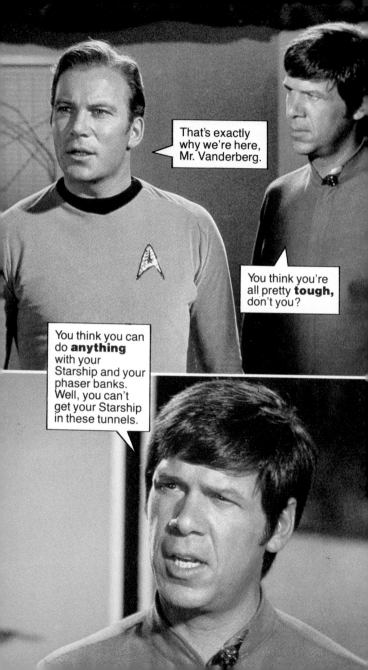

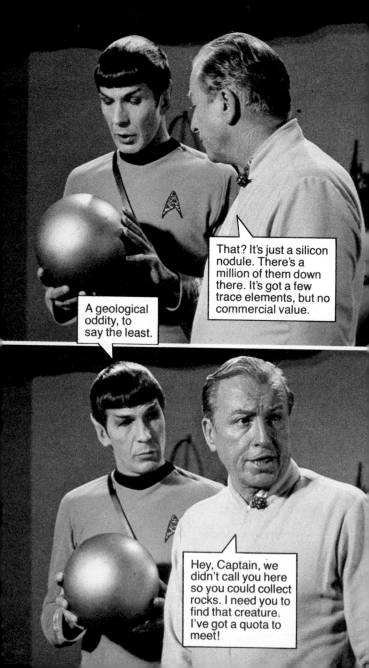

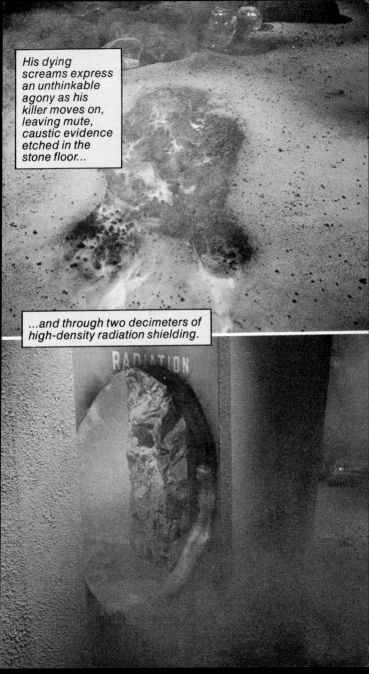

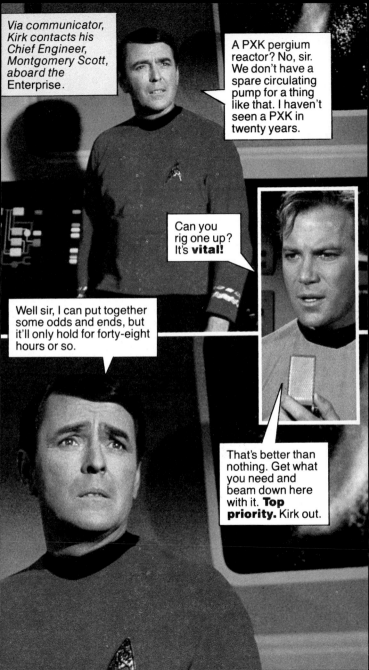

Later, in Vanderberg's office, Kirk, Spock and McCoy evaluate the situation.

The missing pump was not taken by accident. It was the one piece of equipment absolutely essential for the operation of the reactor.

But production facilities have been in operation for over fifty years. Why would the creature have waited so long to try and push the colonists off the planet?

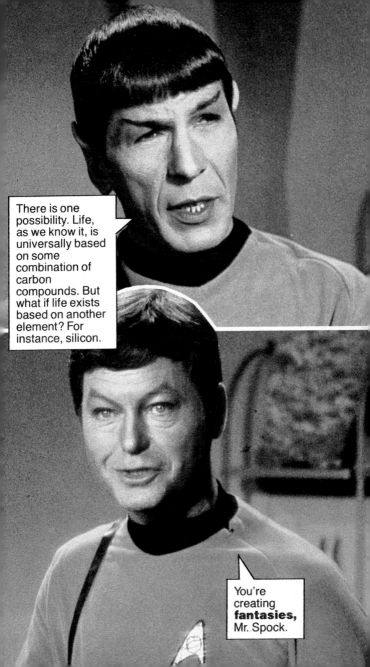

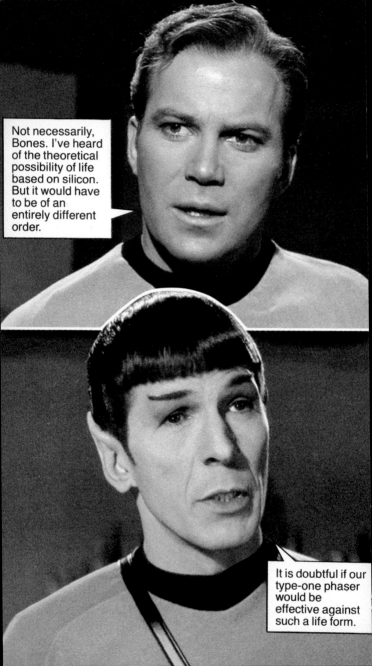

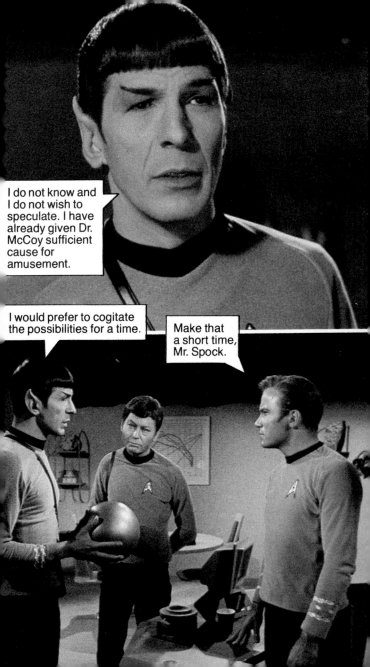

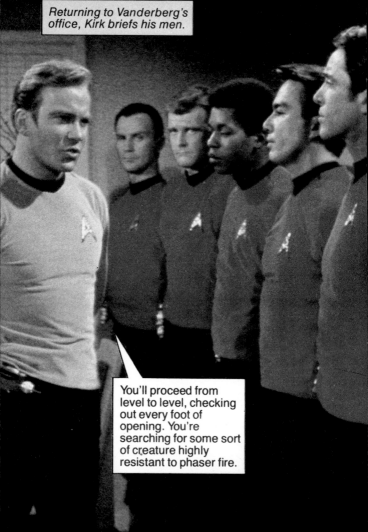

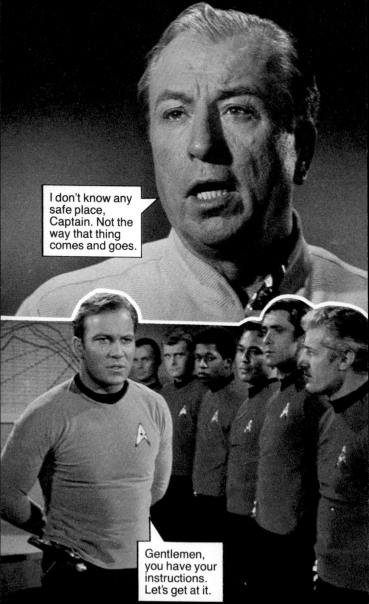

*Following the sound, he rounds a bend in the tunnel...and his blood runs cold as he sees the creature moving toward him, faster than he would have thought possible.*

N...No!!

*An agonized scream rings through the rough-hewn passageway, chilling the marrow of the two seasoned campaigners who hear it.*

That came from just ahead. **Come on!**

Their musings are interrupted by a sudden sound, grating and animate.

Turning, they can feel the hackles rise along the back of their necks as they spot the creature...

...moving fast along the tunnel floor, looking molten yet rock-hard.

They both fire...and hit it, eliciting a cry like that of an anguished bulldozer...

...before it disappears around a bend, moving even faster.

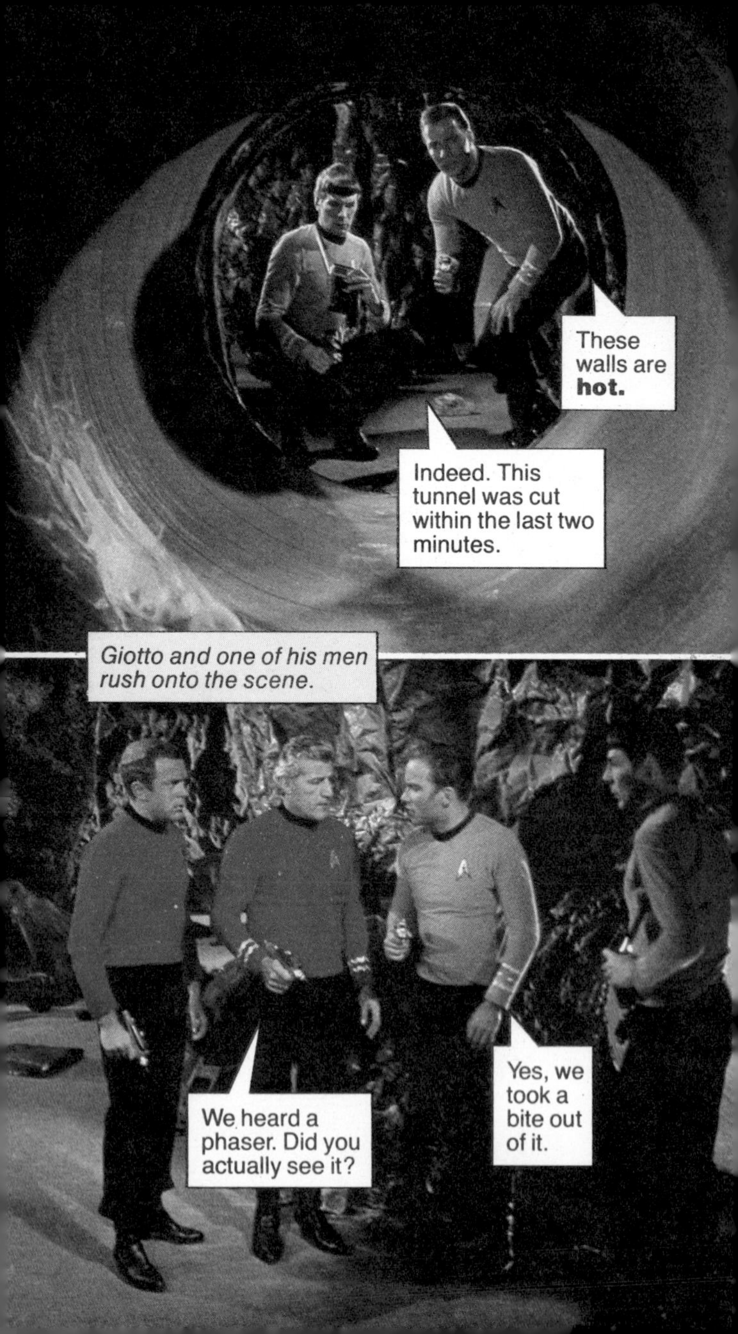
These walls are **hot.**
Indeed. This tunnel was cut within the last two minutes.
*Giotto and one of his men rush onto the scene.*
We heard a phaser. Did you actually see it?
Yes, we took a bite out of it.

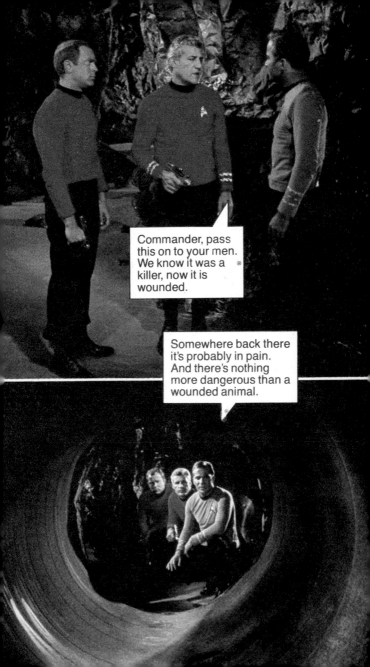

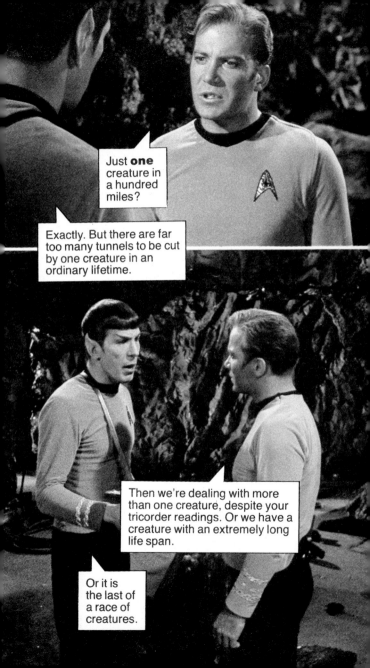

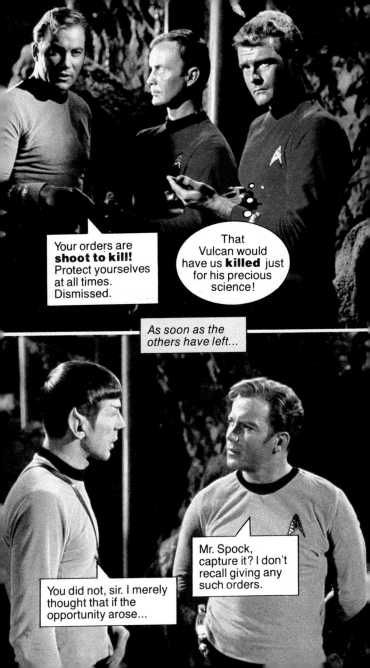

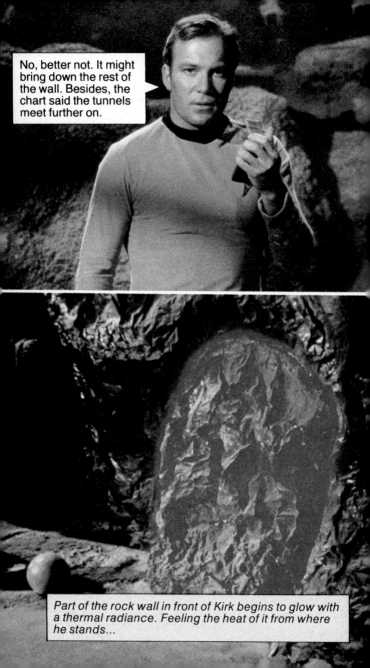

No, better not. It might bring down the rest of the wall. Besides, the chart said the tunnels meet further on.

*Part of the rock wall in front of Kirk begins to glow with a thermal radiance. Feeling the heat of it from where he stands...*

...Kirk watches, fascinated, as the rock dissolves, revealing...

... the killer, the creature responsible for the agonized deaths of over half a hundred men.

*Kirk levels his phaser at the thing as it moves slowly toward him. But some instinct causes him to hold his fire.*

Seeing the wound, Kirk is moved...touched with a curious sympathy. His voice softens.

Well, you **can** be hurt, can't you?

Turning again, the thing sits motionless, presumably regarding Kirk.

Spock is stunned to see his Captain, the man who had given the order "shoot to kill," sitting companionably with the creature that has killed so many.

Except for an ominous pulsing, the creature sits motionless, of unguessable intent.

Facing the creature, Spock prepares to attempt the Mind Touch, a form of telepathy with which most Vulcans can achieve a deep and immediate rapport with another being...

...made possible by an intense focusing of awareness coupled with a receptivity, an utter openness, which must be sustained until...

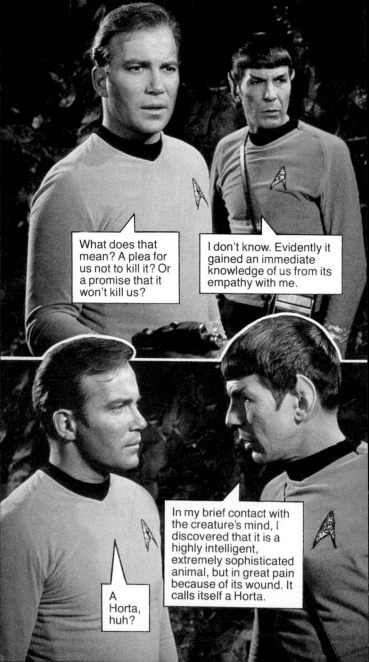

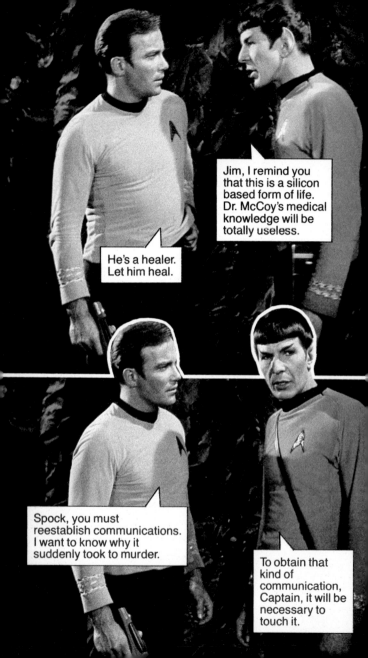

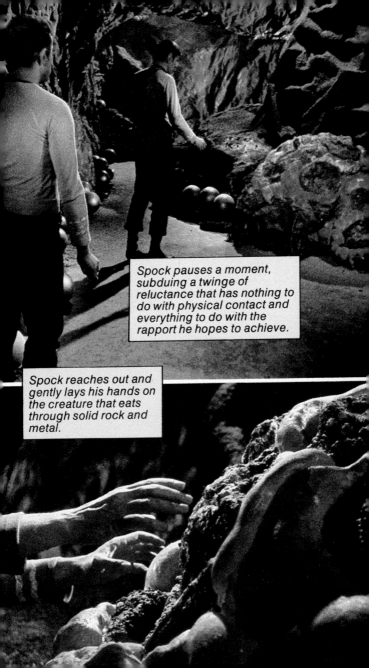

*Spock pauses a moment, subduing a twinge of reluctance that has nothing to do with physical contact and everything to do with the rapport he hopes to achieve.*

*Spock reaches out and gently lays his hands on the creature that eats through solid rock and metal.*

Kirk watches closely, impressed by his First Officer's fortitude...and unaware of the full extent of the danger in which Spock has placed himself.

He's got **guts!**

Even for one at ease with his own id, this merging of identities, this touching of souls, always entails the risk of spiritual trauma, especially with dissimilar life forms.

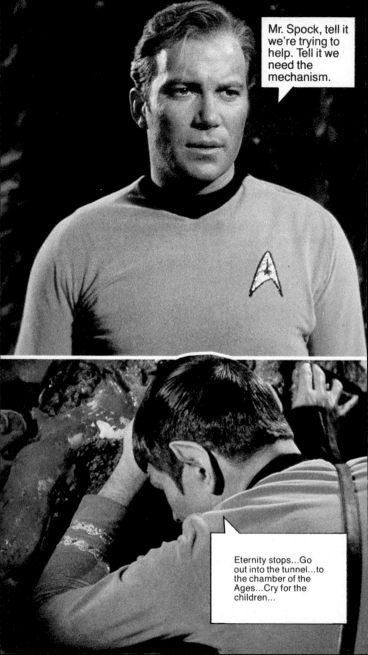

Sadness...go...into the tunnel...there is a passageway...quickly...**go quickly.**

*And Kirk does move quickly, eager to retrieve the mechanism upon which the life-support system of the colony depends.*

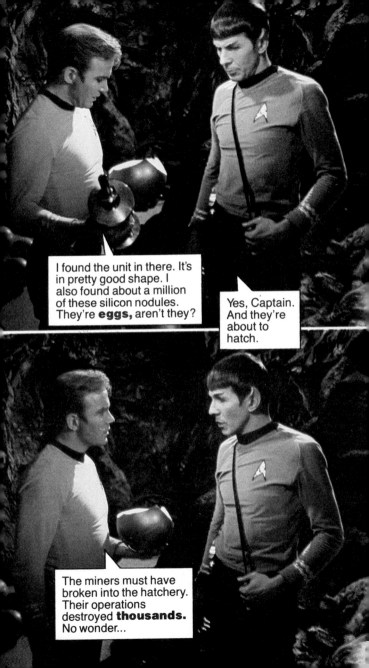

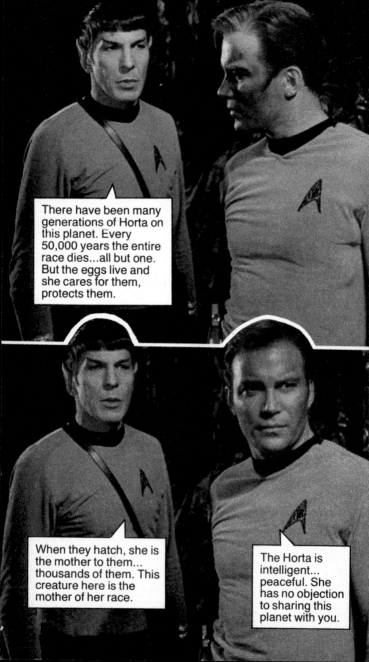

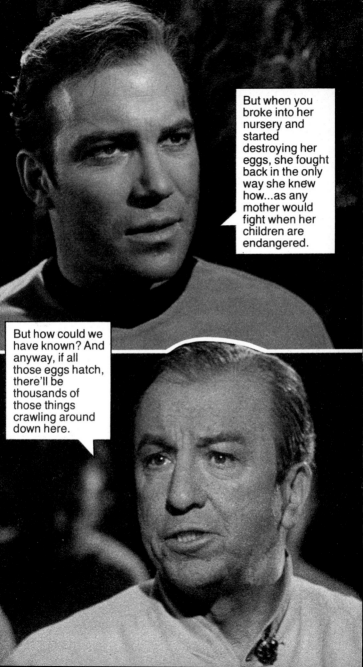

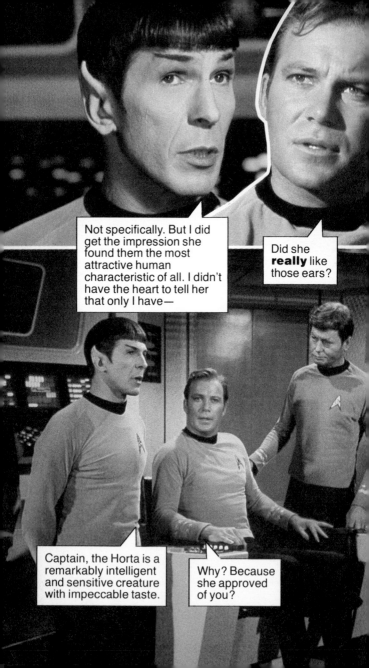

# GLOSSARY

**Captain's Log (or Ship's Log)**—A constantly updated record of a starship's activities, held in the memory banks of the ship's computer.

**Communicator**—A portable intercom unit that fits easily in the palm of the hand. Used primarily for communication among members of a landing party on a planet or for communication with a ship in orbit.

**Horta**—An intelligent, sophisticated silicon life form. Every 50,000 years the entire race dies except one who has been designated to act as the mother of the new race.

**Pergium**—A substance essential to the operation of reactors. Found in abundance deep in the underground mines of Janus VI.

**Phaser**—A weapon based upon the disruption of molecular stability. Used by Star Fleet primarily for defense. The type-one hand phaser is used for self-protection and is taken by landing parties on friendly or diplomatic missions. The type-two phaser pistol may be adapted to a rifle mount for greater range and power.

**PXK Reactor**—An antiquated pergium reactor pump.

**Sensors**—Generic term for any equipment aboard a Starship which is capable of sensing, analyzing, and supplying information about almost anything. This can include composition of an object in space, its dimensions, the presence or absence of life, geological age, etc.

**Security Team**—A division of engineering and support services responsible for maintaining security on ship as well as protecting equipment and personnel on visits to planetside.

**Thermo-Concrete**—Primarily silicon-based substance used for building emergency shelters.

**Starship**—Kirk once remarked that there were only twelve Starships like the Enterprise in the fleet, but his figure is undoubtedly no longer correct, since several Starships have been destroyed and others built and recommissioned.

**Tricorder**—A portable sensor/computer/recorder about the size of a large textbook carried on a shoulder strap. A remarkable device. It can be used to sense, analyze, identify and record almost any data.

**Transporter**—The primary means of moving crew or cargo to and from planet surfaces and other space vessels. It converts matter temporarily into energy, beaming that energy to a fixed point, then reconverting it back into its original molecular structure. Its range is about 16,000 miles.

**United Federation of Planets**—Democratic alliance of solar systems including Sol. All decisions affecting member planets are made through delegates to the Federation Council.

**Vulcans**—Race inhabiting the planet Vulcan recognizable by their pointed ears, upswept eyebrows and sallow complexion. Known for their highly developed intelligence and their denial of the existence of emotion in their lives.

# STAR TREK—DEVIL IN THE DARK QUIZ

**1. The first sign of trouble on Janus VI was:**
 **a.** corroded machinery
 **b.** fatalities among the maintenance crew
 **c.** Schmitter's death
 **d.** the missing circulating pump

**2. The cause of the miners' deaths was:**
 **a.** suffocation
 **b.** chemical corrosion
 **c.** attrition
 **d.** strangulation

**3. When Spock becomes interested in the large round nodule in Vanderberg's office, Vanderberg is not able to tell him:**
 **a.** it is composed of silicon
 **b.** there are millions in the underground tunnels
 **c.** it has no commercial value
 **d.** they are eggs

**4. The Horta's pain is relieved by:**
 **a.** Vulcan Mind-Touch
 **b.** application of thermo-concrete
 **c.** Dr. McCoy's Medical Tricorder
 **d.** millions of silicon nodules

**5. The Horta is a life form based on:**
 **a.** hydrogen
 **b.** silicon
 **c.** carbon
 **d.** cerium

## 6. Gold was discovered on JANUS VI:
   True
   False

## 7. The Horta's life span is:
   **a.** 5,000 years
   **b.** 12,000 years
   **c.** 50-60,000 years
   **d.** 500,000 years

## 8. The miners of Janus VI are happy because the Hortas are:
   **a.** edible
   **b.** saleable
   **c.** extremely efficient miners
   **d.** affectionate

## 9. The Horta attacked the miners because they were destroying:
   **a.** her food supply
   **b.** her tunnels
   **c.** her eggs
   **d.** other Hortas

## 10. Spock thinks the Horta is an intelligent, sensitive creature with impeccable taste because:
   **a.** she dislikes humans
   **b.** she agreed to the miner's proposals
   **c.** she has no emotions
   **d.** she likes Spock's ears

**Turn the page for the answers.**

For three years, the United Federation of Planets has sustained a precarious peace with the Klingon Empire, until an act of wholesale destruction at Beta XIIA fans a flame of hatred that threatens to erupt into all-out interplanetary war. The U.S.S. Enterprise becomes a bloody battleground at warp nine, as Captain Kirk and his crew clash with Kang, the Klingon, in an epic battle for control of the ship.